Key Stage 2

Problem Solving

Steve Mills and Hilary Koll

Name _____

Schofield & Sims

Introduction

What is problem solving? It is applying the different things we know to solve everyday problems or puzzles. The first task is always to understand the information in the problem, and then to decide what mathematics is needed to solve it. In this learning workbook you will learn different ways to approach a variety of problems.

How to use this book

Before you start using this book, write your name in the name box on the first page.

Then decide how to begin. If you want a complete course on problem solving, you should work right through the book from beginning to end. Another way to use the book is to dip into it when you want to find out about a particular topic. The contents page will help you to find the pages you need.

Whichever way you choose, don't try to do too much at once – it's better to work through the book in short bursts.

When you have found the topic you want to study, look out for these icons, which mark different parts of the text:

Activities

This icon shows you the activities that you should complete. You write your answers in the spaces provided. You might find it useful to have some scrap paper to work on for some of the activities. After you have worked through all the activities on the page, turn to pages A1 to A3 at the centre of the book to check your answers. When you are sure that you understand the topic, put a tick in the box beside it on the Contents page.

On pages 11 and 17, you will find **Progress Tests**. These contain questions that will check your understanding of the topics that you have worked through so far. Check your answers on page A4. It is important that you correct any mistakes before moving on to the next section.

At the back of the book you will find a **Final Test**. This will check your understanding of all the topics (page 26).

Explanation

This text explains the topic and gives examples. Make sure you read it before you start the activities.

Scrap Paper

This icon tells you when you may need to use scrap paper to work out your answers.

Fascinating Facts

This text gives you useful background information about the subject.

Contents

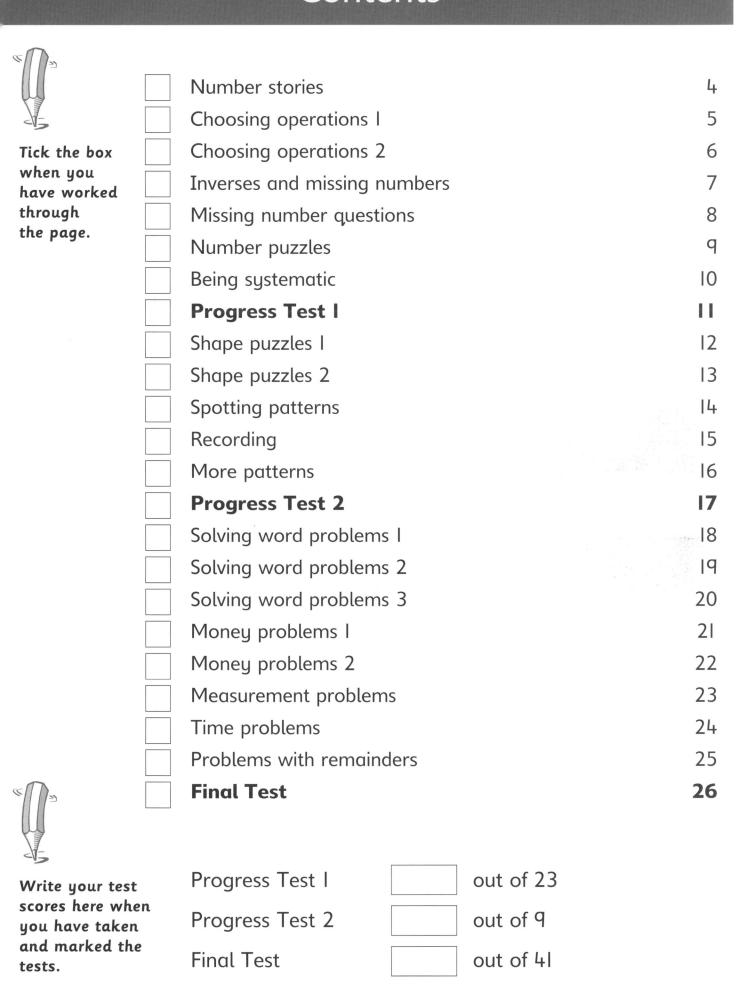

Tick the box when you have worked through the page.

Write your test scores here when you have taken and marked the tests.

Progress Test 1 ☐ out of 23

Progress Test 2 ☐ out of 9

Final Test ☐ out of 41

Number stories

Did you know... An ancient Egyptian document, written over 3000 years ago before the addition and subtraction signs were invented, shows addition as a pair of legs walking forwards and subtraction as a pair of legs walking backwards.

I have walked seven steps and I walk forwards three more steps. **7 + 3**

I have walked seven steps and I walk backwards three steps. **7 – 3**

Number stories

A number story is a story that can also be written as a number fact.

For example, the Ancient Egyptians used the story

I walk seven steps and then forwards three more steps, which is ten steps altogether for the number fact **7 + 3 = 10**

We can use any real life situation to make a number story for a number fact.

These stories are both for the number fact **3 × 4 = 12**

- *Three dogs each have four legs. This makes twelve legs altogether.*

- *There are four plates on a table. Three tomatoes are put on each plate. Twelve tomatoes are used.*

1. Write the number fact for each of these stories.

    a) *I had £10 and gave £3 to my sister, leaving me with £7.* _____

    b) *My dad shared fifteen sweets equally between three of us.*
       We each got five sweets. _____

    c) *Five chairs in my kitchen each have four legs.*
       This is twenty legs altogether. _____

2. Make up a number story for each of these facts.

    a) $9 - 3 = 6$ _____

    b) $2 \times 4 = 8$ _____

    c) $12 \div 2 = 6$ _____

Choosing operations 1

Did you know...? Addition, subtraction, multiplication and division are all called **'operations'**. An operation is when we do something with numbers.
These are the operation signs   + – × ÷

1. For each of these number stories choose the correct operation sign to complete the number fact.

a) There were six potatoes in a bag. Four got used.
Two potatoes were left.

$$6 \boxed{} 4 = 2$$

b) A tricycle has three wheels. Six tricycles have eighteen wheels.

$$3 \boxed{} 6 = 18$$

c) Three ladybirds were on a leaf. One flew away, now there are two.

$$3 \boxed{} 1 = 2$$

d) My dad had ten sweets. He shared them out between two people. They each got five sweets.

$$10 \boxed{} 2 = 5$$

Choosing the right operation to solve a problem

A number story can also be made into a question, like this...

Number story

- There were six potatoes in a bag. Four got used.
Two potatoes were left.

$$6 - 4 = 2$$

Question

- There were six potatoes in a bag. Four got used.
How many were left?

$$6 - 4 = ?$$

2. Answer these number story questions:

a) A bicycle has two wheels.
How many wheels do five bicycles have?   _____

b) Seven ladybirds were on a leaf.
Two flew away, now how many are there?   _____

c) My dad had eight sweets. He shared them out between two people. How many did they each get?   _____

d) Nine people were on a bus. Six more got on.
How many are on the bus, now?   _____

Choosing operations 2

Choosing the right operation to complete a number fact

If you are given a number fact without an operation sign you can use the information below to help you work out which sign is missing:

The following statements are true where all the numbers in the number fact are positive whole numbers:

If you add or multiply, the answer will be the largest number in the number fact

$5 + 3 = 8$	$11 + 9 = 20$	$201 + 47 = 248$
$3 \times 5 = 15$	$8 \times 2 = 16$	$25 \times 5 = 125$

If you subtract or divide, the first number will be the largest in the number fact

$24 - 4 = 20$	$50 - 49 = 1$	$100 - 32 = 68$
$24 \div 6 = 4$	$50 \div 2 = 25$	$100 \div 25 = 4$

1. Fill in the missing operation sign to make these number facts correct.

a) $50 \boxed{} 2 = 25$ b) $50 \boxed{} 2 = 48$ c) $50 \boxed{} 2 = 100$

d) $45 \boxed{} 15 = 60$ e) $30 \boxed{} 2 = 32$ f) $64 \boxed{} 2 = 128$

g) $55 \boxed{} 75 = 130$ h) $42 \boxed{} 6 = 7$ i) $38 \boxed{} 19 = 19$

2. Now make up a number story for facts 'a' to 'f' in activity **1**.

a) _____

b) _____

c) _____

d) _____

e) _____

f) _____

Inverses and missing numbers

Inverses

We call the operation that undoes another operation its inverse.

For example, if we add **5** then we can subtract **5** to 'undo' it.

Subtraction is the **inverse** of **addition**	$17 + 5 = 22$ $22 - 5 = 17$
Addition is the **inverse** of **subtraction**	$17 - 3 = 14$ $14 + 3 = 17$
Division is the **inverse** of **multiplication**	$4 \times 3 = 12$ $12 \div 3 = 4$
Multiplication is the **inverse** of **division**	$20 \div 5 = 4$ $4 \times 5 = 20$

1. What is the inverse operation for:

    a) division? _____

    b) subtraction? _____

    c) addition? _____

    d) multiplication? _____

Missing number questions

We can use inverses to help us solve missing number questions:

$37 + \boxed{} = 69$ In an **addition** fact like this, we know that the **answer** is the **largest number**, so the missing number must be **smaller than 69**

Use the **inverse** operation. **Subtraction** is the inverse of **addition**.

$69 - 37 = 32$ so the missing number is **32**

$\boxed{} \div 5 = 7$ In a **division** fact like this, we know that the **first number** is the **largest**, so the missing number must be **larger than 7**

Use the **inverse** operation. **Multiplication** is the inverse of **division**.

$7 \times 5 = 35$ so the missing number is **35**

2. Work out the missing number in each of these number facts.

    a) $65 + \boxed{} = 96$ **b)** $6 \times \boxed{} = 30$ **c)** $\boxed{} - 54 = 11$

    d) $\boxed{} \div 4 = 8$ **e)** $\boxed{} + 16 = 30$ **f)** $\boxed{} \times 4 = 28$

Missing number questions

Watch out for missing number subtractions and divisions where the missing number is the second number, like these:

$55 - \boxed{} = 31$ In a **subtraction** fact like this, we know that the **first number** is the **largest**, so the missing number must be **smaller than 55**

Here we do **NOT** need to use the inverse operation. Adding would make the number larger than **55**. We can just rearrange the subtraction, like this:

$55 - 31 = \boxed{}$ so the missing number is **24**

$36 \div \boxed{} = 4$ In a **division** fact like this, we know that the **first number** is the **largest**, so the missing number must be **smaller than 36**

Here we do **NOT** need to use the inverse operation. Multiplying would make the number larger than **36**. We can just rearrange the division, like this:

$36 \div 4 = \boxed{}$ so the missing number is **9**

1. Work out the missing number by rearranging the subtraction or division.

a) $65 - \boxed{} = 21$ b) $16 \div \boxed{} = 8$ c) $30 - \boxed{} = 16$

$\boxed{}\,\square\,\boxed{} = \boxed{}$ $\boxed{}\,\square\,\boxed{} = \boxed{}$ $\boxed{}\,\square\,\boxed{} = \boxed{}$

d) $20 \div \boxed{} = 5$ e) $74 - \boxed{} = 23$ f) $45 \div \boxed{} = 5$

$\boxed{}\,\square\,\boxed{} = \boxed{}$ $\boxed{}\,\square\,\boxed{} = \boxed{}$ $\boxed{}\,\square\,\boxed{} = \boxed{}$

2. Work out the missing numbers. For some you will need to use inverses.

a) $32 + \boxed{} = 47$ b) $3 \times \boxed{} = 27$ c) $55 - \boxed{} = 42$

d) $\boxed{} \div 3 = 6$ e) $\boxed{} + 23 = 30$ f) $\boxed{} \times 2 = 14$

g) $\boxed{} - 35 = 41$ h) $74 - \boxed{} = 23$ i) $18 \div \boxed{} = 2$

Number puzzles

 **Did you know...?** Karl Friedrich Gauss (1776–1855) was a mathematical genius. It is said that by the time he was **3** years old he had taught himself how to read and write.

When Gauss was about **10** years old his class was set a number puzzle by his primary school teacher. The teacher wanted to keep the pupils busy for a while so asked them to add together all the numbers from **1** to **100**.

Gauss came up with the correct answer in less than a minute. How did he do it?

 Look at **this** puzzle:

Find the total of all the numbers from 1 to 9
(find pairs that make 10)

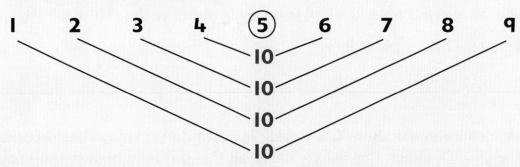

4 pairs that make 10 and the number ⑤ in the middle makes
40 + 5 = 45

 1. Find the total of all the numbers from:

a) **11** to **19**
(find pairs that make 30)
11 12 13 14 ⑮ 16 17 18 19
⌣30⌣

b) **21** to **29**
(find pairs that make 50)
21 22 23 24 ㉕ 26 27 28 29
⌣50⌣

c) **1** to **19** (find pairs that make 20)
1 2 3 4 5 6 7 8 9 ⑩ 11 12 13 14 15 16 17 18 19
⌣20⌣

d) **1** to **24** (find pairs that make 25 – there is no middle number this time)
1 2 3 4 5 6 7 8 9 10 11 12 13 14 15 16 17 18 19 20 21 22 23 24
\25/

 2. Can you work out the answer to Gauss's problem using the same method?

Being systematic

Be systematic when solving a puzzle. Being systematic means working through in a sensible order, like this:

Find all the possible pairs of whole numbers with a total of 10

0 + 10	and	10 + 0
1 + 9	and	9 + 1
2 + 8	and	8 + 2
3 + 7	and	7 + 3
4 + 6	and	6 + 4
5 + 5		

> Notice that the numbers have been written in order.

1. Find all the possible pairs of whole numbers with a total of **14**

   0 + 14   and   **14 + 0**

2. Four children, Ali, Ben, Cam and Dev stand in a row. Their initials are A, B, C and D. Finish this list to show all the possible orders they could stand in. Notice how they are arranged systematically.

A B C D	B A C D	C A B D	D A __ __
A B D C	B A D C	C A __ __	__ __ __ __
A C B D	B C C D	C B A D	D B __ __
A C D B	B C D C	C B __ __	__ __ __ __
A D B C	B D A C	C D C D	D C __ __
A D C B	B D __ __	__ __ __ __	__ __ __ __

3. Write all six possible orders of writing the letters X, Y, Z. Be systematic.

4. Three **odd** numbers are added to make **9**. Find all the different sets of odd numbers with a total of **9**. Be systematic.

   1 + 1 + ___

   1 + ___ + ___

Progress Test 1

1. Write the number fact for each of these stories.

   a) *I had £15 and gave £7 to my sister, leaving me with £8.* _____

   b) *Three chairs in my kitchen each have four legs.*
   This is twelve legs altogether. _____

2. Make up a number story for each of these facts.

   a) 5 × 4 = 20 _____

   b) 16 ÷ 2 = 8 _____

3. Answer these number story questions.

   a) Nine ladybirds were on a leaf. Three flew away.
   How many are there now? _____

   b) Fifteen people were on a bus. Eight more got on.
   How many are on the bus now? _____

4. Fill in the missing operation sign to make these correct.

   a) 100 ☐ 2 = 50   **b) 100 ☐ 2 = 98**   **c) 100 ☐ 2 = 200**

   d) 45 ☐ 15 = 60   **e) 30 ☐ 2 = 32**   **f) 64 ☐ 2 = 128**

5. What is the inverse operation for:

   a) division? _____   **b)** addition? _____

6. Work out the missing numbers. For some you will need to use inverses
and others you will need to rearrange the subtraction or division.

   a) 32 + ☐ = 47   **b) 3 × ☐ = 27**   **c) 58 − ☐ = 42**

   d) ☐ ÷ 3 = 7   **e) ☐ + 16 = 30**   **f) ☐ × 2 = 18**

7. Find the total of all the numbers from:

   a) 1 to 9   **b) 25 to 35**

   1 2 3 4 5 6 7 8 9   **25 26 27 28 29 30 31 32 33 34 35**

8. Find all the possible pairs of whole numbers with a total of **13**.

Being systematic in shape puzzles

When exploring shape puzzles, be systematic by working through in a sensible order, like this:

This fruit tray has spaces for 4 apples. Sketch all the ways that the tray could look if <u>none, one, two, three or four</u> apples are in it.

Start with no apples:

Now one apple:

Now two apples:

Now three apples:

And finally four: Total = **16** ways

 1. This shape is made from squares of different sizes.

Count the total number of squares in this shape. Be systematic.

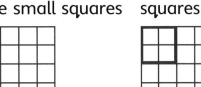

Start by counting the small squares

Then the **2 × 2** squares

Then the **3 × 3** squares

And finally the **4 × 4** square

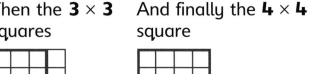

Total = _____ squares

 **2.** This shape is made from triangles of different sizes.

Count the total number of triangles in this shape. Be systematic.

Total = _____ triangles

Shape puzzles 2

Congruent halves

When a shape is copied exactly, we have two congruent shapes. We can rotate (turn) a shape and it is still congruent, like this:

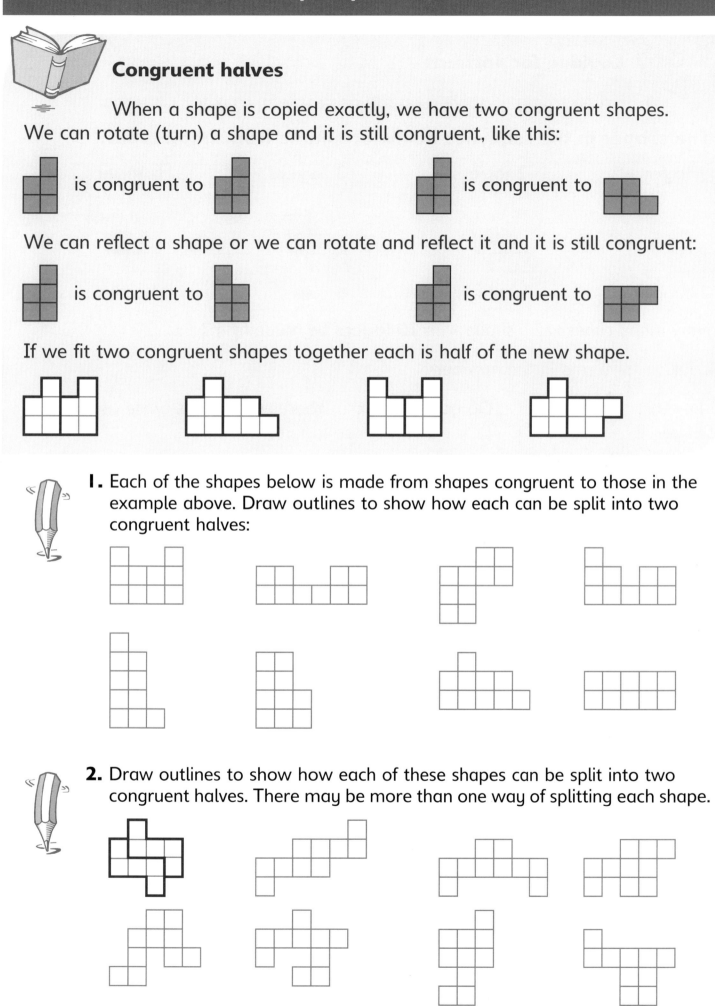

is congruent to   is congruent to

We can reflect a shape or we can rotate and reflect it and it is still congruent:

is congruent to   is congruent to

If we fit two congruent shapes together each is half of the new shape.

1. Each of the shapes below is made from shapes congruent to those in the example above. Draw outlines to show how each can be split into two congruent halves:

2. Draw outlines to show how each of these shapes can be split into two congruent halves. There may be more than one way of splitting each shape.

Spotting patterns

Looking for patterns

When trying to solve a puzzle or problem, look for patterns:

The shapes in the sequence below are made from small cubes.

1 layer   **2 layers**   **3 layers**   **4 layers**

                       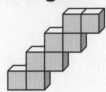

2 cubes   4 cubes   6 cubes   8 cubes

How many cubes will a shape with **10 layers** *be made from?*

Look for patterns in the numbers:

Layer 1 = 2 cubes	Do you notice that there are always twice as many
Layer 2 = 4 cubes	cubes as there are layers?
Layer 3 = 6 cubes	
Layer 4 = 8 cubes	So the shape with **10 layers** must have **20 cubes**

1. How many cubes will **Shape 10** be made from?

Shape 1   **Shape 2**   **Shape 3**   **Shape 4**   **...Shape 10?**

3 cubes   6 cubes   _____ cubes   _____ cubes   _____ cubes

2. How many dots will **Pattern 10** be made from?

Pattern 1   **Pattern 2**   **Pattern 3**   **Pattern 4**   **...Pattern 10?**

         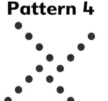   

4 dots   8 dots   _____ dots   _____ dots   _____ dots

3. Make up a set of shapes made from dots and work out how many dots will be in the **10**th shape.

Answers to Activities

Page 4
1. a) $10 - 3 = 7$
   b) $15 \div 3 = 5$
   c) $5 \times 4 = 20$
2. 3 appropriate number stories

Page 5
1. a) $6 - 4 = 2$
   b) $3 \times 6 = 18$
   c) $3 - 1 = 2$
   d) $10 \div 2 = 5$
2. a) 10
   b) 5
   c) 4
   d) 15

Page 6
1. a) $\div$ b) $-$ c) $\times$
   d) $+$ e) $+$ f) $\times$
   g) $+$ h) $\div$ i) $-$
2. 6 appropriate number stories

Page 7
1. a) multiplication
   b) addition
   c) subtraction
   d) division
2. a) 31   b) 5   c) 65
   d) 32   e) 14   f) 7

Page 8
1. a) $65 - 21 = 44$
   b) $16 \div 8 = 2$
   c) $30 - 16 = 14$
   d) $20 \div 5 = 4$
   e) $74 - 23 = 51$
   f) $45 \div 5 = 9$
2. a) 15   b) 9   c) 13
   d) 18   e) 7   f) 7
   g) 76   h) 51   i) 9

Page 9
1. a) 135
   b) 225
   c) 190
   d) 300
2. $50 \times 101 = 5050$

Page 10
1. $0 + 14$ $14 + 0$
   $1 + 13$ $13 + 1$
   $2 + 12$ $12 + 2$
   $3 + 11$ $11 + 3$
   $4 + 10$ $10 + 4$
   $5 + 9$ $9 + 5$
   $6 + 8$ $8 + 6$
   $7 + 7$
2. Table completed with a total of 24 distinct answers.
3. XYZ   YXZ   ZYX
   XZY   YZX   ZXY
4. $1+1+7$, $1+7+1$, $7+1+1$,
   $1+3+5$, $1+5+3$,
   $3+1+5$, $3+5+1$,
   $5+1+3$, $5+3+1$,
   $3+3+3$

Page 12
1. $16 + 9 + 4 + 1 = 30$ squares
2. $9 + 3 + 1 = 13$ triangles

Page 13
1.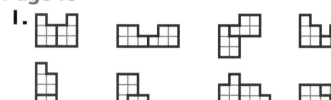

2. Possible answers:

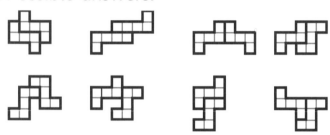

Page 14
1. 30
2. 40
3. Answers will depend on the design.

Page 15
1.

Totals	Number
0	1
1	1
2	2
3	2
4	3
5	3
6	4
7	3
8	3
9	2
10	2
11	1
12	1

Page 16
1. a)
1	1
2	4
3	9
4	16

b) 100

2. a)
1	4
2	8
3	12
4	16

b) 40

3. a)
1	1
2	4
3	9
4	16

b) 100

Page 18
1. a) division
   b) multiplication
   c) division
   d) addition
2. a) addition
   b) division

Page 19
1. a) 144
   b) 6839
   c) 30
   d) 480
   e) 728

Answers to Activities

Page 20
1. a) 97
   b) 33
   c) 8
   d) 100
2. a) 34
   b) 27
   c) 15
   d) 68

Page 21
1. a) £3.58
   b) £7.22
   c) £9.43
   d) £12.06
2. a) 34p
   b) £35
   c) £1200
   d) £4
   e) £8.80
3. a) 15p
   b) 44p
   c) £5
   d) 8p

Page 22
1. a) 452p
   b) 300p
   c) 320p
   d) 905p
   e) 212p
   f) 496p
   g) 1200p
   h) 2000p

2. a) £3.12
   b) £4.50
   c) £1.83
   d) £2.70
   e) £4
   f) £10
   g) £15.05
   h) £30
3. a) £34.80 or 3480p
   b) £9.65 or 965p
   c) £4.10 or 410p
   d) £0.50 or 50p
   e) £3.27 or 327p

Page 23
1. a) 20cm
   b) 1200g
   c) 240ml
   d) 35km
   e) 120m
2. a) 8
   b) 1·75kg or 1750g
   c) 4km

Page 24
1. a) 10:15 p.m.
   b) 7:10 p.m.
   c) 3:00 p.m.
   d) 2:40 p.m.
   e) 07:02
2. a) 50 minutes
   b) 8 hours 30 minutes
   c) 10 hours 10 minutes

Page 25
1. a) 8
   b) 7
   c) 15
   d) 7
   e) 12
   f) 8
   g) 13

Answers to Tests

PROGRESS TEST 1 – Page 11

1. a) 15 − 7 = 8
   b) 3 × 4 = 12
2. two suitable number stories
3. a) 6
   b) 23
4. a) ÷   b) −   c) ×
   d) +   e) +   f) ×
5. a) multiplication
   b) subtraction
6. a) 15   b) 9   c) 16
   d) 21   e) 14   f) 9
7. a) 45   b) 330
8. 0 + 13   13 + 0
    1 + 12   12 + 1
    2 + 11   11 + 2
    3 + 10   10 + 3
    4 + 9   9 + 4
    5 + 8   8 + 5
    6 + 7   7 + 6

Total marks = 23

PROGRESS TEST 2 – Page 17

1.

2.

3.

2	3	4	5	6	7
3	4	5	6	7	8
4	5	6	7	8	9
5	6	7	8	9	10
6	7	8	9	10	11
7	8	9	10	11	12

4. a) 1   5
      2   10
      3   15
      4   20
   b) 50
5. 1, 4, 9, 16, 25, 36, 49, 64, 81, 100

Total marks = 9

FINAL TEST – Pages 26 to 28

1. a) 23 − 8 = 15
   b) 5 × 4 = 20
2. a) 30
   b) 37
3. a) ×   b) −   c) +
4. a) 25   b) 9   c) 13
   d) 32   e) 7   f) 8
5. 30
6. 15 + 0   0 + 15
    14 + 1   1 + 14
    13 + 2   2 + 13
    12 + 3   3 + 12
    11 + 4   4 + 11
    10 + 5   5 + 10
     9 + 6   6 + 9
     8 + 7   7 + 8
7. Possible answers:

8. 1, 4, 9, 16, 25, 36, 49, 64, 81, 100
9.

10. a) 1   4
       2   8
       3   12
       4   16
    b) 40
11. a) 103   b) 28
12. a) 51p   b) 60p
13. a) £5.68   b) £12.04
14. a) £11.85   b) £3.36   c) £3.06
15. a) 5   b) 3kg   c) 22 000g
16. a) 6:15 p.m.
    b) 2:55 p.m.
    c) 19:25
17. a) 11   b) 10   c) 12

Total marks = 41

Recording

On page **10** we saw how important it is to be systematic when solving problems. It is also very important to record the results of your work clearly.

Recording your work can help you to see patterns and avoid mistakes.

We can use tables or charts to set our work out clearly. Can you see which type of recording for this puzzle is better?

Count the total number of squares in this shape.

Size of squares	Number
1 × 1	16
2 × 2	9
3 × 3	4
4 × 4	1
Total	30

Little squares 16
Bigger squares 9
even bigger 4 Big 1
total = 30

1. Complete this table to show the results of the problem.
Here is a full set of dominoes. Each domino has a total number of dots. For each total from 0 to 12, how many dominoes are there?

Totals	Number
0	1
1	1
2	2
3	
4	
5	
6	
7	
8	
9	
10	
11	
12	

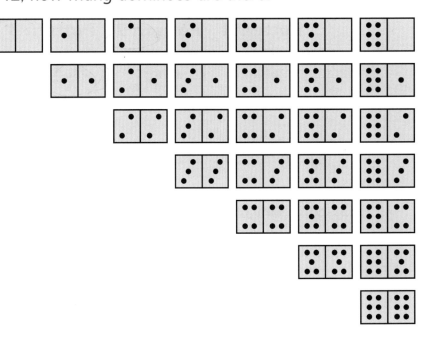

More patterns

Did you know...?

Square numbers are called square because they can be drawn as squares.

They are the result of multiplying a number by itself, like this:

| 1 | 4 | 9 | 16 | 25 | 36 |

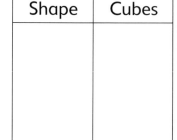

$1 \times 1 = 1,$ $2 \times 2 = 4,$ $3 \times 3 = 9,$ $4 \times 4 = 16,$ $5 \times 5 = 25,$ $6 \times 6 = 36$

Watch out for square numbers when looking for patterns:

1. a) Count the number of cubes in each shape.
Record the results in the table

Shape 1 **Shape 2** **Shape 3** **Shape 4**

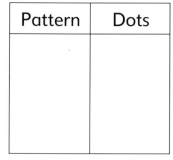

Shape	Cubes

b) How many cubes will **Shape 10** be made from? _____

2. a) Count the number of dots in each pattern.
Record the results in the table

Pattern 1 **Pattern 2** **Pattern 3** **Pattern 4**

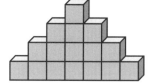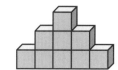

Pattern	Dots

b) How many dots will **Pattern 10** be made from? _____

3. a) Count the number of stars in each pattern.
Record the results in the table

Pattern 1 **Pattern 2** **Pattern 3** **Pattern 4**

Pattern	Stars

b) How many stars will **Pattern 10** be made from? _____

Progress Test 2

1. Draw outlines to show how each can be split into two congruent halves.

 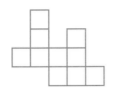 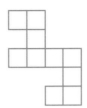

2. Be systematic when solving this problem:
*This egg box has spaces for **6** eggs. Shade **all** the ways that the box could look if **one** or **two** eggs are in it.*

3. Complete this table to show the results of the problem.
Two dice are rolled and the total is found. What are the possible totals?

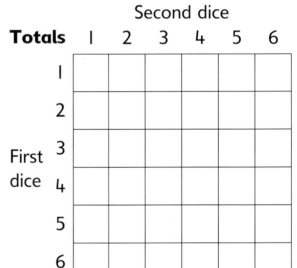

Totals	Second dice					
	1	2	3	4	5	6
First dice 1						
2						
3						
4						
5						
6						

4. a) Count the number of cubes in each shape. Record the results in the table

Shape 1   Shape 2   Shape 3   Shape 4

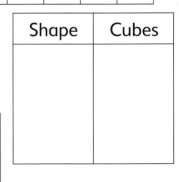

Shape	Cubes

b) How many cubes will **Shape 10** be made from? _____

5. Write the first **10** square numbers. _____

Useful words

When looking at word problems look out for these words. They can sometimes give you a clue about what to do.

Addition: **plus, and, add, altogether, total, increase by, more, sum**

Subtraction: **take away, less, difference, minus, decrease by, fewer, left**

Multiplication: **product, multiply, groups of, times, double, twice, squared**

Division: **divide, share, half, halve, quarter, remainder**

I. Look for useful words and **say which operation** you think you would use to solve these word problems:

	Word Problem	Operation
a)	James is **42** years old and his daughter is half his age. How old is she?	division
b)	Some children get into groups of **4.** There are **8** groups. How many children are there?	
c)	My dad has eight sweets. He shares them between four of us. How many do we each get?	
d)	Fifteen people were on a bus. Eleven more got on. Now how many are on the bus?	

Watch out – although these words can often tell you what to do, always think carefully about the problem because you can be **tricked**! Look at this...
I went swimming four times last week and three times this week – How many times did I go swimming?
Notice that this is an **addition** question even though the word **times** appears!

2. Which **operation** would you use? Think carefully about these – you may be tricked!

	Word Problem	Operation
a)	Pete has **10** fewer stickers than Jane. Pete has **25.** How many does Jane have?	
b)	**24** children in a class get into groups of **4.** How many groups are there?	

Solving word problems 2

When faced with a problem, follow these steps:

- **Read the problem carefully.**
- **Look for any useful words in the question**
- **Write down any important numbers in the question**
- **Decide what operations to use**
- **Get an approximate answer**
- **Decide whether to use a written or mental method and work it out**
- **Finally check your answer**

3363 adults and **4762** children were at a theme park.

How many people were at the theme park?

- Important numbers   **3363   4762**
- I will add the two numbers
- Approximately **3000 + 5000** = about **8000**
- Work it out :   **3363**   (written method)

    $+$ **4762**

    8125   → Now check whether **8125** people is about right.

I. Solve these word problems using the steps listed above. Think carefully, and use scrap paper, if you need to.

a) There are three times as many cars in a car park on Monday than on Sunday. **48** cars were parked here on Sunday. How many cars are there on Monday? _____

b) **9543** people visited the Coliseum cinema this year. This was **2704** more than last year. How many people visited the cinema last year? _____

c) Ella's mum is five times older than Ella. Ella is **6**. How old is her mum? _____

d) A library has **80** books on each shelf. There are **6** shelves. How many books are there? _____

e) A car park has **785** spaces of which **57** are empty. How many cars are in the car park? _____

Tackling problems

Some problems have **one step** – where there is only one operation, like this one:

41 birds are in a tree. **25** more arrive. How many are in the tree now?

You could solve it like this...   **41 + 25 = 66**

Some problems have **two steps**, like this:

41 birds are in a tree. **25** more arrive but **13** leave. How many are in the tree now?

You could solve it like this...

Step one   **41 + 25 = 66**   Step two   **66 – 13 = 53**

Or like this...

Step one   **25 – 13 = 12**   Step two   **41 + 12 = 53**

1. Solve these one-step word problems.

a) **82** cars are in the car park. **15** more arrive.
How many cars are there now?   _____

b) A teacher has **18** grey pencils and **15** coloured pencils.
How many pencils does she have in total?   _____

c) My mum is four times older than me. She is **32**.
How old am I?   _____

d) There are **5** shelves. A supermarket has **20** tins
of beans on each shelf. How many tins are there?   _____

2. Solve these two-step word problems.

a) **25** cars are in the car park. **8** leave but **17** more arrive.
How many cars are there now?   _____

b) A teacher has **18** grey pencils and **15** coloured pencils.
She gives away **6** pencils. How many pencils does she
have in total now?   _____

c) My mum is three times older than me. She is **30**.
How old will I be in **5** years time?   _____

d) There are **5** shelves. A supermarket has **20** tins of
beans on each shelf. **32** tins get sold. How many tins
are there now?   _____

Money problems 1

Did you know... Did you know that it is wrong to write amounts of money using both the pounds and the pence signs?

This is wrong £5.87p ✗

Decimal point ↓

£5.87

If the amount has a decimal point just use the pound sign.

1. Write these amounts correctly using a pound sign and a decimal point.

   a) Three pounds and fifty-eight pence.   _____

   b) Seven pounds and twenty-two pence.   _____

   c) Nine pounds and forty-three pence.   _____

   d) Twelve pounds and six pence.   _____

2. Solve these one-step money problems.

   a) I had **58**p and I spent **24**p. How much do I have left?   _____

   b) Ben was given £**20** for his birthday and £**15** for Christmas. How much did he get in total?   _____

   c) Jack is paid £**100** every month. How much does he earn in a year (**12** months)?   _____

   d) Grandma emptied her money box and shared the amount between her three grandchildren. The box had £**12**. How much did each child get?   _____

   e) A burger costs £**2.20**. Mr Wildman buys four burgers for his children. How much does he pay?   _____

3. Solve these two-step money problems.

   a) I had **49**p. I was given **20**p more and then I spent **54**p. How much do I have left?   _____

   b) Six apples cost **66**p. How much does it cost to buy **4** apples?   _____

   c) Amy saves £**1.50** of her pocket money each week. After **10** weeks she buys a CD costing £**10**. How much money does she have left after that?   _____

   d) Jo buys a pencil costing **48**p and a rubber costing **24**p. How much less than **80**p is this?   _____

Money problems 2

There are 100 pence in every pound.

Multiply by 100 to change pounds to pence
Divide by 100 to change pence to pounds

£4	=	400p
£3.42	=	342p
£3.05	=	305p
1200p	=	£12

1. How many pence is:

a) £4.52 _452p_   b) £3 _____   c) £3.20 _____   d) £9.05 _____

e) £2.12 _____   f) £4.96 _____   g) £12 _____   h) £20 _____

2. Write these amounts in pounds:

a) 312p _£3.12_   b) 450p _____   c) 183p _____   d) 270p _____

e) 400p _____   f) 1000p _____   g) 1505p _____   h) 3000p _____

Watch the units

Sometimes in money problems two amounts are given, but one might be given in **pounds** and the other might be given in **pence**. Be careful!

Make sure you change the numbers so that they are both in pounds, or both in pence, like this:

I have a £20 note and I buy a chew costing 10p. How much change do I get?

Watch out – the answer is not **20 – 10 = 10**. We must change them both to be in pounds or both to be in pence:

£20.00 – £0.10 = £19.90   or   **2000p – 10p = 1990p**

3. Solve these money problems, changing the amounts to pounds or pence.

a) I have £35 and I spend 20p. How much do I have now? _____

b) Three items cost 40p, £3.25 and £6.
   What is the total cost?   _____

c) I had £4.52. I was given 8p more and then I spent 50p.
   How much do I have left?   _____

d) James saves 80p of his pocket money each week.
   After 10 weeks he buys a CD costing £7.50.
   How much money does he have left?   _____

e) Jo buys a pencil costing 68p and a rubber costing £1.05
   How much change does she get from £5?   _____

Measurement problems

Length, mass and capacity

Word problems sometimes involve measurements, such as

25cm,   **10**m,   **3**km,   **3**kg,   **400**g,   **250**ml,   **6**l

Remember to give the unit when you give your answer.

1. Solve these measurement problems.

   a) I have a piece of string that is **80**cm long.
   I cut it into four equal pieces. How long is each piece? _____

   b) A tin of beans weighs **400**g.
   How much do three tins weigh? _____

   c) I pour **300**ml of water into a cup and drink **60**ml.
   How much water is left in the cup? _____

   d) A runner ran **5**km every day for a week.
   How many kilometres did he run in total? _____

   e) A square field has fencing all the way around its perimeter.
   One side of the field is **30**m. How much fencing is there? _____

Watch the units

Sometimes in measurement problems, like with money problems, two amounts are given in different units. Be careful!

Make sure you change the numbers so that they are both in the same unit.

2. Solve these problems.

   a) I have a piece of string that is **2**m long. I need pieces of
   string that are **25**cm long. How many pieces can I cut? _____

   b) Three items weigh **1**kg, **250**g and **0.5**kg.
   What is the total mass of the three items? _____

   c) A runner ran **500**m every day for **20** days.
   How much further than **6**km did he run in total? _____

   d) There are **2·2**kg of sugar in a bag.
   How many grams are there in **5** bags? _____

Time problems

Calculating with time

You may be asked to find how long a programme or event goes on for and when it started or finished. **Do not** use a calculator when dealing with time – you'll get the wrong answer!

A '1 hour **40** minute' TV programme starts at **9:30** a.m. What time does it end?

Approach it like this: Add or subtract the whole hours first and then count on or count back the extra minutes.

9:30 a.m. + **1** hour → **10:30** a.m. ... then **count on 40** mins... → **11:10 a.m.**

A '**2** hour **45** minute' tennis match ends at **5:25** p.m. What time did it start?

5:25 p.m. – **2** hours → **3:25** p.m. ... then **count back 45** mins... → **2:40 p.m.**

If the time now is **21:27**, what time will it be in **3** hours **20** minutes?

21:27 + **3** hours → **00:27**... then **count on 20** mins... → **00:47**

1. Solve these problems in the same way.

   a) A '**1** hour **45** minute' TV programme starts at **8:30** p.m. What time does it end? _____

   b) A '**2** hour **20** minute' TV programme starts at **4:50** p.m. What time does it end? _____

   c) A '**3** hour **5** minute' tennis match ends at **6:05** p.m. What time did it start? _____

   d) A '**2** hour **15** minute' tennis match ends at **4:55** p.m. What time did it start? _____

   e) If the time now is **22:50**, what time will it be in **8** hours **12** minutes? _____

2. Solve these problems.

   a) A cake went in the oven at **10:25** a.m. and came out at **11:15** a.m. How long was it in the oven? _____

   b) A man went to work at **8:45** a.m. and finished at **5:15** p.m. How long was he at work? _____

   c) A girl went to sleep at **20:55** and woke at **07:05** the next morning. How long did she sleep for? _____

Remainders

When you are faced with a problem that involves division, it is important to watch out for **remainders**.

*How many **4**s in **22**?   Answer = **5** remainder **2***

This question can be solved by doing **22 ÷ 4**, and the answer is **5 r 2**

Remainders don't always make sense. Look at this problem:

22 *children are going on a school trip. Each car can carry **4** children.*

How many cars will be needed?

Which is right?

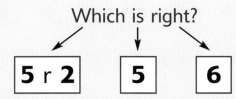

The answer is **6**, because, although there will be only **2** children in the sixth car, that car is still needed.

Watch out for remainders and think carefully about what they mean in each problem.

In some problems you will need to round up the next whole number and in others you will need to round down to the previous whole number.

1. Solve these problems.

    a) **46** eggs are put into boxes that each hold **6** eggs. How many boxes are needed? _____

    b) **46** eggs are put into boxes, that each hold **6** eggs. How many boxes will be full? _____

    c) A school has £**62** to buy netballs. Each ball costs £**4**. How many can they buy? _____

    d) I have **52** cakes. Each box holds **8** cakes. How many boxes do I need? _____

    e) **45** children are going on a school trip. Each car can carry **4** children. How many cars will be needed? _____

    f) A florist has **43** roses. She puts them into vases with **5** roses in each vase. How many full vases are there? _____

    g) Each page of a photo album holds **6** photos. What is the smallest number of pages that I need to hold **74** photos? _____

Final Test

1. Write the number fact for each of these stories.

    a) *I had £23 and gave £8 to my sister, leaving me with £15.* _____

    b) *Five sheep each have four legs. This is twenty legs altogether.* _____

2. Answer these number story questions.

    a) **24** cows were in a field. Six more joined them,
    how many are there now?   _____

    b) **32** people were on a bus. Five more got on.
    How many are on the bus now?   _____

3. Fill in the missing operation sign to make these correct.

    a) 40 ☐ 2 = 80   **b)** 40 ☐ 2 = 38   **c)** 40 ☐ 2 = 42

4. Work out the missing numbers. For some you will need to use inverses and others you will need to rearrange the subtraction or division.

    a) 27 + ☐ = 52   **b)** 4 × ☐ = 36   **c)** 66 − ☐ = 53

    d) ☐ ÷ 4 = 8   **e)** ☐ + 43 = 50   **f)** ☐ × 4 = 32

5. Find the total of all the numbers from **1** to **19**.

    1 2 3 4 5 6 7 8 9 10 11 12 13 14 15 16 17 18 19

6. Write all the possible pairs of whole numbers with a total of **15**.

7. Draw outlines to show how each can be split into two congruent halves. There may be more than one way of splitting each shape.

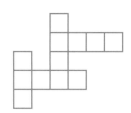   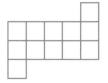   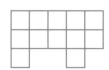   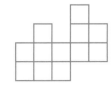

8. Write the first **10** square numbers.

_____

9. Be systematic when solving this problem:
This fruit box has spaces for **4** peaches. Shade **all** the ways that the box could look if **none, one, two, three or four** peaches are in it.

10. a) Count the number of cubes in each shape.
Record the results in the table

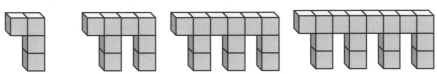

Shape 1   Shape 2   Shape 3   Shape 4

Shape	Cubes

b) How many cubes will **Shape 10** be made from? _____

11. Solve these one-step word problems.

a) **66** cars are in the car park. **37** more arrive.
How many cars are there now? _____

b) My mum is four times older than me. I am seven.
How old is my mum? _____

12. Solve these two-step money problems.

a) I had **58**p. I was given **30**p more and then
I spent **37**p. How much do I have left? _____

b) Six apples cost **72**p. How much does it
cost to buy five apples? _____

13. Write these amounts correctly using a pound sign and a decimal point.

a) Five pounds and sixty-eight pence _____

b) Twelve pounds and four pence _____

14. Solve these money problems, changing the amounts to pounds or pence.

   a) Three items cost **50**p, **£3.35** and **£8**.
What is the total cost of the three items? _____

   b) I had **£4.52**. I was given **9**p more and then
I spent **£1.25**. How much do I have left? _____

   c) Jo buys a coffee costing **85**p and a cake costing
£1.09. How much change from **£5** does she get? _____

15. Solve these measurement problems.

   a) I have a piece of string that is **2**m long. I need
pieces of string that are each **40**cm long.
How many pieces can I cut? _____

   b) Three items weigh **2**kg, **200**g and **0·8**kg.
What is the total mass of the three items? _____

   c) There are **2·2**kg of sugar in a bag.
How many grams are there in **10** bags? _____

16. Solve these time problems.

   a) A 'I hour **25** minute' TV programme starts at
4:50 p.m. What time does it end? _____

   b) A '2 hour **10** minute' tennis match ends at
5:05 p.m. What time did it start? _____

   c) If the time now is **13:35**, what time will it be
in **5** hours **50** minutes? _____

17. Solve these problems, thinking carefully about remainders.

   a) A school has **£47** to buy netballs. Each ball costs **£4**.
How many can they buy? _____

   b) I have **73** cakes. Each box holds **8** cakes.
How many boxes do I need? _____

   c) A florist has **63** daffodils. She puts them into vases
with **5** daffodils in each vase. How many full vases
are there? _____